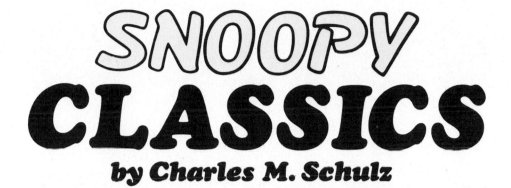

SNOOPY CLASSICS

by Charles M. Schulz

BOOK CLUB ASSOCIATES
LONDON

This edition published 1982 by Book Club Associates by arrangement with Hodder & Stoughton Children's Books.

Printed in Belgium by Henri Proost, Turnhout, Belgium.

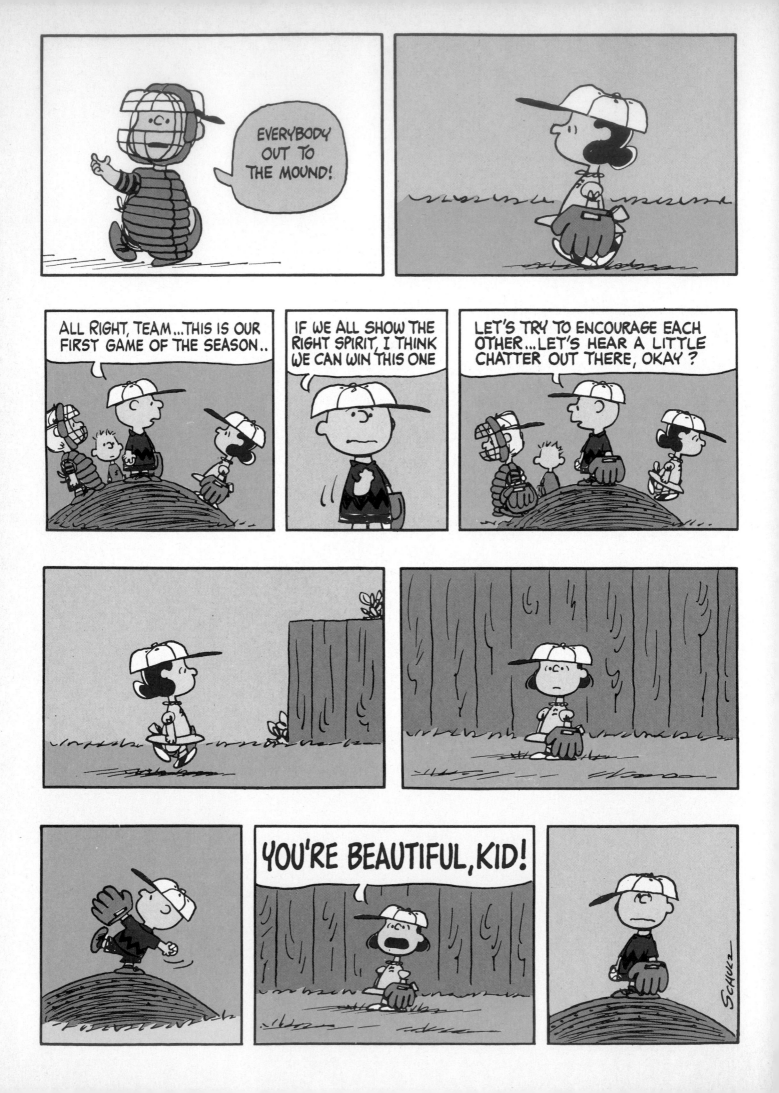

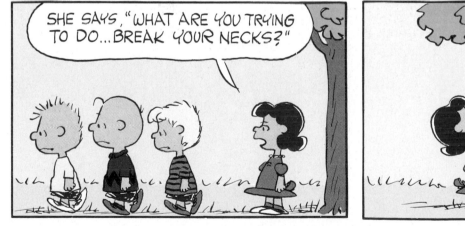

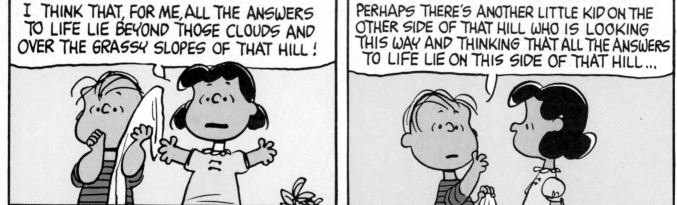

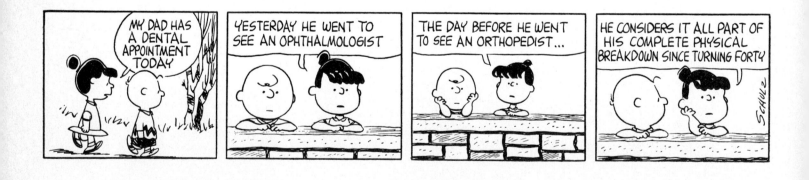

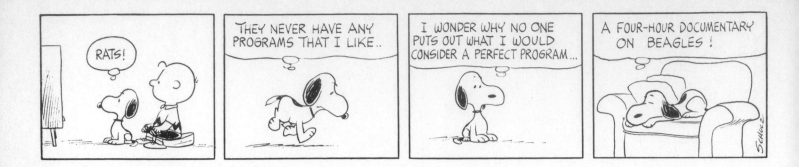

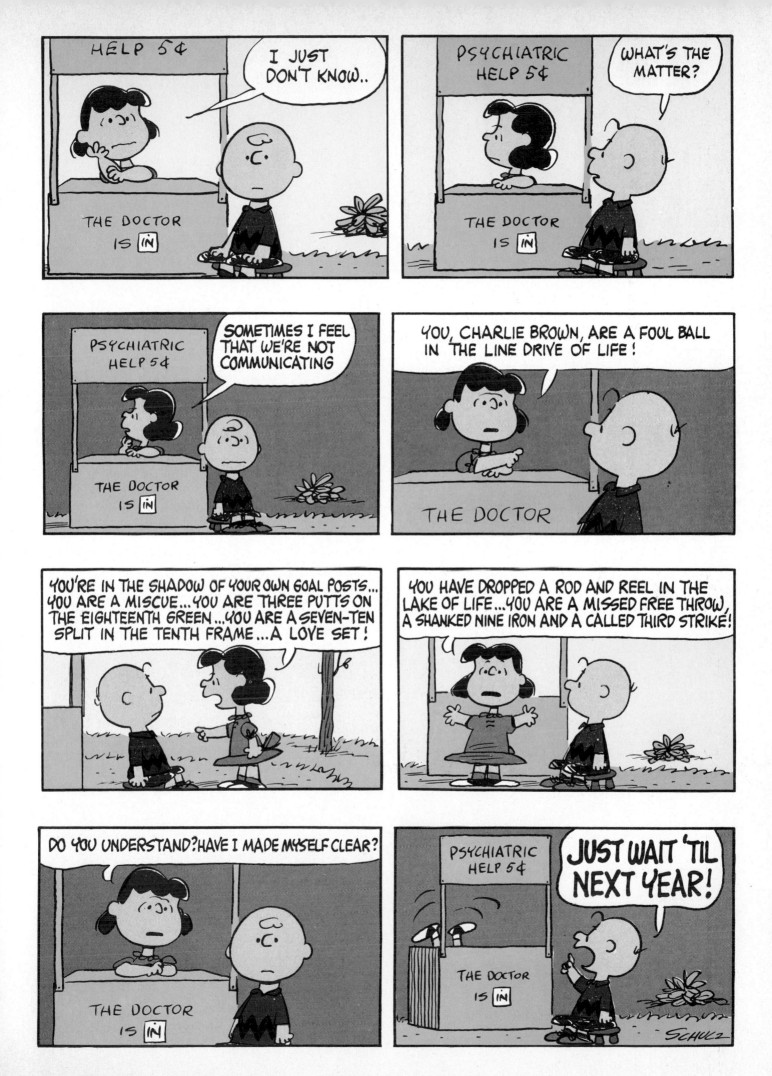

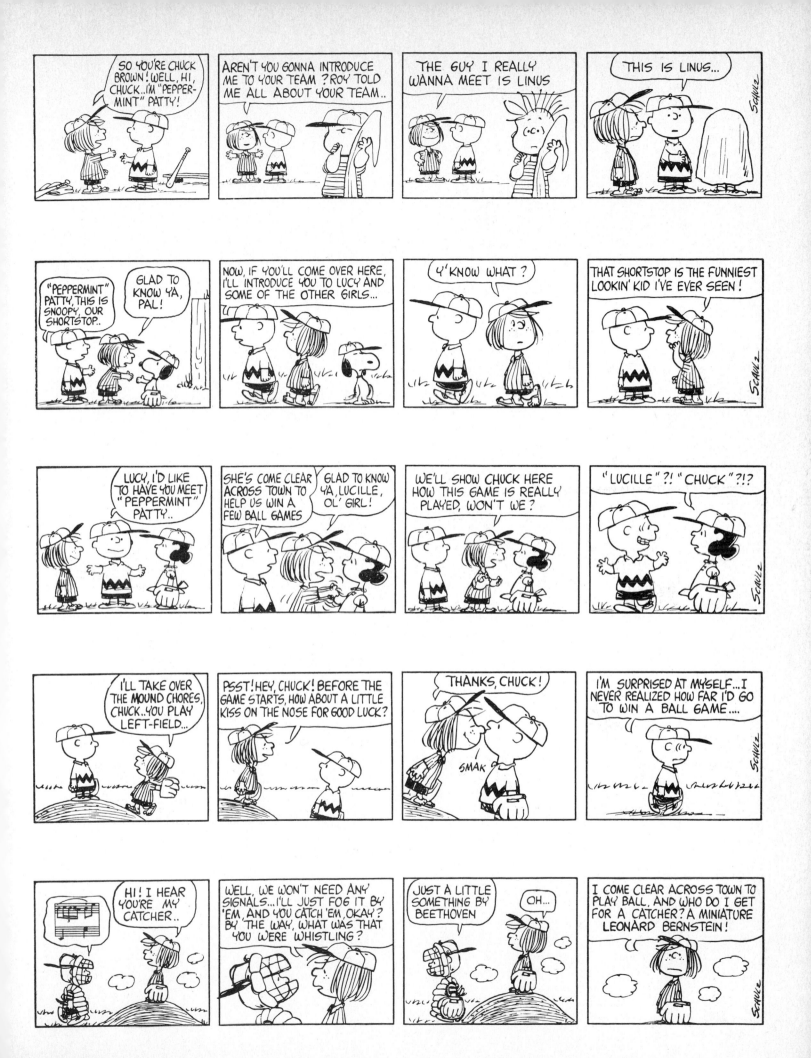

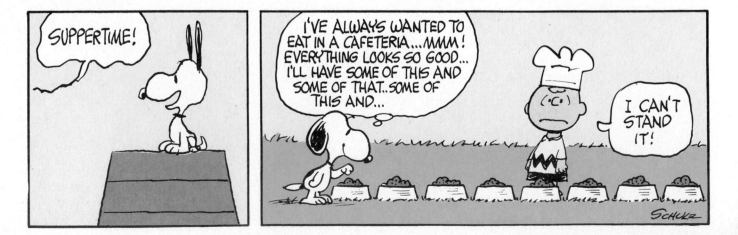

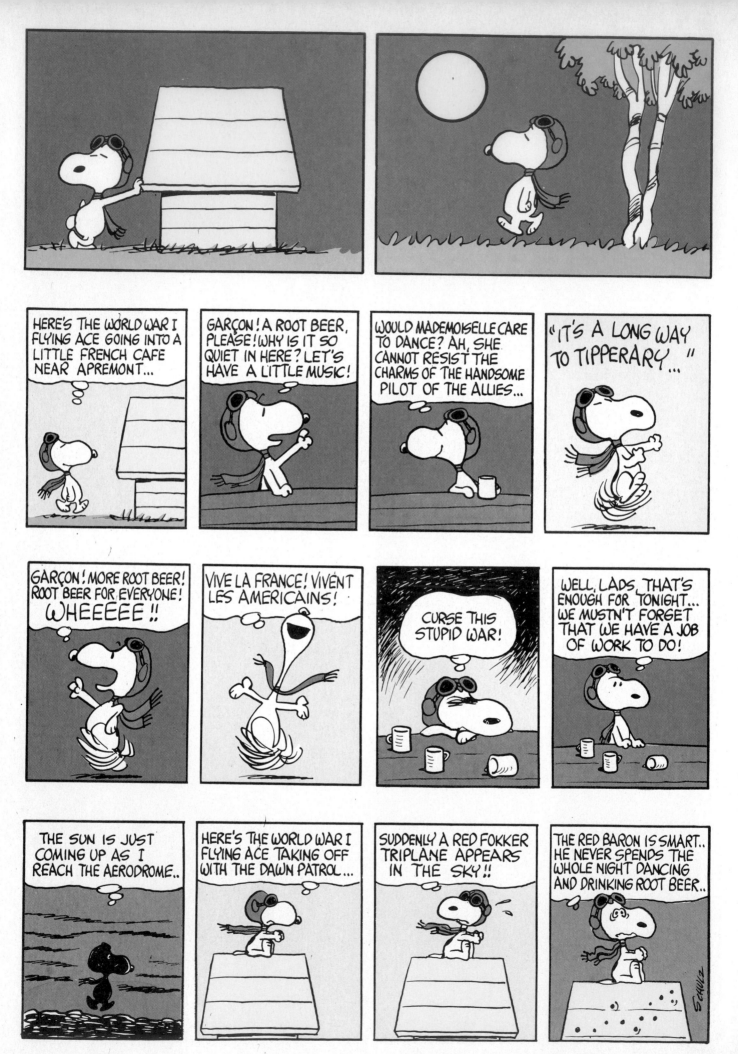

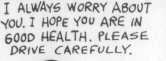